Flute Exam Pack

ABRSM Grade 1

Selected from the 2018–2021 syllabus

C000155669

Contents

page

LIST A

1	**Johann Krieger** Bourrée: from *Sechs musicalische Partien*, arr. Richard Jones	2
2	**Johannes Brahms** Cradle Song, Op. 49 No. 4, arr. Ian Denley	3
3	**Giuseppe Verdi** La donna è mobile (The woman is fickle): from *Rigoletto*, arr. Nancy Litten	4

LIST B

1	**Roma Cafolla** Lazy Sunday: from *Playaround* for Flute, Book 3	5
2	**Scott Joplin** The Easy Winners, arr. David Blackwell	6
3	**Mark Tanner** The Pelican from Heligan: No. 1 from *Creature Comforts*, Grades 1–3	7

LIST C

1	**Mark Nightingale** Click Here: No. 2 from *Jazz@Etudes* for Flute	8
2	**Wilhelm Popp** Study in F: from *Erster Flöten-Unterricht*, Op. 387	9
3	**James Rae** Snow Walk: No. 1 from *42 More Modern Studies for Solo Flute*	10

Scales and arpeggios	11
Sight-reading	13

Consultant Editor for ABRSM: David Blackwell
Footnotes: Anthony Burton and Richard Jones (RJ)

Other pieces for Grade 1

LIST A
4   **Attwood** Andante (from *Sonatina No. 3*), arr. Denley. *Time Pieces for Flute, Vol. 1* (ABRSM)
5   **O'Carolan** Dermot O'Dowd, arr. Denley. *Time Pieces for Flute, Vol. 1* (ABRSM)
6   **Daquin** Noël, arr. McDowall. *Harlequin, Book 1* (Cramer)
7   **Haydn** Minuet, arr. Barratt. *Grade by Grade, Flute Grade 1* (Boosey & Hawkes)
8   **Susato** Rondo VI, arr. Rosenberg. *Grade by Grade, Flute Grade 1* (Boosey & Hawkes)
9   **Sholom Secunda** Donna Donna, arr. Lawrance (*observing repeat*). *Winner Scores All for Flute* (Brass Wind)
10 **Trad. Scottish** The Blue Bell of Scotland (arr.). *What Else Can I Play? Flute Grade 1* (Faber)

LIST B
4   **Bart** I'd do anything (from *Oliver!*), arr. Lawrance. *Winner Scores All for Flute* (Brass Wind)
5   **Andrew Lloyd Webber** Close Every Door to Me (from *Joseph and the Amazing Technicolor Dreamcoat*), arr. Lawrance. *Winner Scores All for Flute* (Brass Wind)
6   **Alan Haughton** Budgie *or* The Secret Garden: from *Fun Club for Flute, Grade 0–1* (Kevin Mayhew)
7   **Helen Long** Spooked. *Grade by Grade, Flute Grade 1* (Boosey & Hawkes)
8   **Cecilia McDowall** Moulin Rose *or* Zig Zag. *Harlequin, Book 1* (Cramer)
9   **Julian Nott** Theme from *Wallace and Gromit*, arr. Hammond. *Ten Top Pops for Flute* (Kevin Mayhew)
10 **R. & R. Sherman** Hushabye Mountain (from *Chitty Chitty Bang Bang*) (arr.). *What Else Can I Play? Flute Grade 1* (Faber)

LIST C
4   **Alan Bullard** Sad Flute *or* Bouncy Flute: No. 2 *or* No. 5 from *Fifty for Flute, Book 1* (ABRSM)
5   **Paul Harris** Study in C *or* Study in G. No. 4 *or* No. 5 from *76 Graded Studies for Flute, Book 1* (Faber)
6   **Klosé** Study in G. No. 7 from *More Graded Studies for Flute, Book 1* (Faber)
7   **A. J. Mears** Under the Rainbow. No. 8 from *More Graded Studies for Flute, Book 1* (Faber)
8   **E. Köhler** Study in G *or* Study in C. No. 5 *or* No. 6 from *125 Easy Classical Studies for Flute* (Universal)
9   **Philip Sparke** Modal Melody *or* Lullaby: No. 3 *or* No. 6 from *Skilful Studies for Flute* (Anglo Music)
10 **Lynne Williams** Sad Song *or* Articulate: No. 6 *or* No. 8 from *Thirty One Two Three Flute Studies* (Forton Music)

First published in 2017 by ABRSM (Publishing) Ltd,
a wholly owned subsidiary of ABRSM, 4 London Wall Place,
London EC2Y 5AU, United Kingdom
© 2017 by The Associated Board of the Royal Schools of Music
Distributed worldwide by Oxford University Press

Music origination by Julia Bovee and Katie Johnston (Sight-reading)
Cover by Kate Benjamin & Andy Potts
Printed in England by Caligraving Ltd, Thetford, Norfolk
on materials from sustainable sources.
P14410

A:1

Bourrée

from *Sechs musicalische Partien*

Arranged and edited
by Richard Jones

Johann Krieger
(1651–1735)

Here is a good example of a bourrée: a fairly quick and lively French dance, though in this case written by a German composer. The dance type is in duple time, so would be felt as two minim beats per bar, despite the time signature. This Bourrée was originally a keyboard piece – it belonged to a collection of dances by Johann Krieger for spinet or clavichord. (RJ) **The first repeat should be observed in the exam**, but the ornaments are optional.

Source: *Sechs musicalische Partien* (Nuremberg: W. M. Endter, 1697). In this arrangement, the original keyboard right-hand part is played on the flute, the keyboard left hand remains unchanged, and the new keyboard right hand is editorial. All dynamics, slurs, staccatos and ornaments are editorial suggestions only.

Cradle Song

Op. 49 No. 4

A:2

Arranged by Ian Denley

Johannes Brahms
(1833–97)

Brahms composed his famous 'Lullaby', originally called *Wiegenlied* or 'Cradle Song', in 1868 for his Viennese friends Arthur and Bertha Faber, to celebrate the birth of their son Hans. The gently rocking accompaniment is based on a popular Viennese love song which Bertha had sung to Brahms ten years earlier, when she was a 17-year-old member of a Ladies' Choir which he conducted. Brahms wrote to the couple that he imagined Bertha singing Hans to sleep while Arthur murmured a love song to her.

© 1998 by The Associated Board of the Royal Schools of Music
Adapted from *Time Pieces for Flute*, Volume 1, selected and arranged by Ian Denley (ABRSM)

The woman is fickle

La donna è mobile

from *Rigoletto*

A:3

Arranged by Nancy Litten

Giuseppe Verdi
(1813–1901)

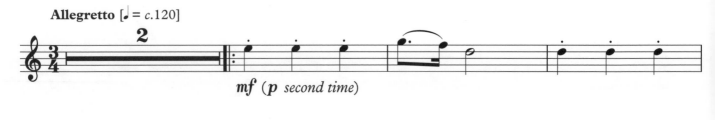

Verdi's 1851 opera *Rigoletto* is set in the 16th century in the north Italian city of Mantua. The plot centres on the arrogant, immoral Duke of Mantua, his court jester Rigoletto and Rigoletto's daughter Gilda. The aria 'La donna è mobile' is sung in Act III by the Duke in a tavern. The staccato markings in the melodic line help give the piece its swagger.

Lazy Sunday

from *Playaround* for Flute, Book 3

Roma Cafolla
(born 1949)

B:1

Roma Cafolla is a Northern Irish composer. Amongst the large amount of educational music she has written are the graded *Playaround* volumes. The swung quavers give this piece a mood of weekend relaxation, but also notice the metronome marking: the piece may not be as lazy as you think!

© Forton Music 2014
Reproduced by permission from *Playaround* for Flute, Book 3.

B:2

The Easy Winners

Arranged by David Blackwell

Scott Joplin
(1867/8–1917)

Scott Joplin grew up in Texas, the son of a former slave, and became, as he called himself, 'the King of Ragtime Writers' – a pioneer in print of the ragtime style, which combines the regular tread of marches and dances with the syncopations of African American tradition. This is the first strain of a 'ragtime two-step', which he published in St Louis in 1901. The tempo marking 'Not fast' is an instruction which Joplin repeated in many publications. Note, too, that the classic ragtime style is not thought to have involved swung rhythms: even quavers give the piece its characteristic strutting movement.

The Pelican from Heligan

No. 1 from *Creature Comforts*, Grades 1–3

Mark Tanner
(born 1963)

Mark Tanner is a well-known British pianist in concert halls and on cruise liners; he has also taught at school and college level, written reviews and articles for many magazines, as well as a book called *The Mindful Pianist*, and composed more than sixty albums of educational music. This is the first item in a graded collection of 'animal-inspired pieces': The Lost Gardens of Heligan are a popular visitor attraction in Cornwall, England, but the pelican is a rare bird in the county, so the title must have been chosen for its pleasing sound! The composer says that the piece is 'both quirky and fun to play; its recurring jaunty rhythms encourage quite a laid-back approach, but are best suited to a firmly rooted tempo'.

C:1

Click Here

No. 2 from *Jazz@Etudes* for Flute

Mark Nightingale
(born 1967)

Mark Nightingale is a well-known jazz trombonist, the leader of several groups including a Big Band, whose repertoire features his own compositions and arrangements, and also much in demand as a member of other bands. He has written many studies and concert pieces for various instruments. In this study, with its computer-inspired title, the rests are as important as the notes.

Flute Exam Pieces

ABRSM Grade 1

Selected from the 2018–2021 syllabus

Piano accompaniment

Contents

page

LIST A

1	**Johann Krieger** Bourrée: from *Sechs musicalische Partien*, arr. Richard Jones	2
2	**Johannes Brahms** Cradle Song, Op. 49 No. 4, arr. Ian Denley	3
3	**Giuseppe Verdi** La donna è mobile (The woman is fickle): from *Rigoletto*, arr. Nancy Litten	4

LIST B

1	**Roma Cafolla** Lazy Sunday: from *Playaround* for Flute, Book 3	5
2	**Scott Joplin** The Easy Winners, arr. David Blackwell	6
3	**Mark Tanner** The Pelican from Heligan: No. 1 from *Creature Comforts*, Grades 1–3	8

Consultant Editor for ABRSM: David Blackwell
Footnotes: Anthony Burton and Richard Jones (RJ)

Editorial guidance

We have taken the pieces in this book from a variety of sources. Where appropriate, we have edited the pieces to help you prepare for your performance. We have added metronome markings (in square brackets) and ornament realizations. Details of other changes or suggestions are given in the footnotes. These editorial additions are for guidance only: you do not have to follow them in the exam.

First published in 2017 by ABRSM (Publishing) Ltd,
a wholly owned subsidiary of ABRSM, 4 London Wall Place,
London EC2Y 5AU, United Kingdom
© 2017 by The Associated Board of the Royal Schools of Music
Distributed worldwide by Oxford University Press

Music origination by Julia Bovee
Cover by Kate Benjamin & Andy Potts
Printed in England by Caligraving Ltd, Thetford, Norfolk
on materials from sustainable sources.

Bourrée

from *Sechs musicalische Partien*

Arranged and edited
by Richard Jones

Johann Krieger
(1651–1735)

Here is a good example of a bourrée: a fairly quick and lively French dance, though in this case written by a German composer. The dance type is in duple time, so would be felt as two minim beats per bar, despite the time signature. This Bourrée was originally a keyboard piece – it belonged to a collection of dances by Johann Krieger for spinet or clavichord. (RJ) **The first repeat should be observed in the exam**, but the ornaments are optional.

Source: *Sechs musicalische Partien* (Nuremberg: W. M. Endter, 1697). In this arrangement, the original keyboard right-hand part is played on the flute, the keyboard left hand remains unchanged, and the new keyboard right hand is editorial. All dynamics, slurs, staccatos and ornaments are editorial suggestions only.

Cradle Song

Op. 49 No. 4

Arranged by Ian Denley

Johannes Brahms
(1833–97)

A:2

Brahms composed his famous 'Lullaby', originally called *Wiegenlied* or 'Cradle Song', in 1868 for his Viennese friends Arthur and Bertha Faber, to celebrate the birth of their son Hans. The gently rocking accompaniment is based on a popular Viennese love song which Bertha had sung to Brahms ten years earlier, when she was a 17-year-old member of a Ladies' Choir which he conducted. Brahms wrote to the couple that he imagined Bertha singing Hans to sleep while Arthur murmured a love song to her.

© 1998 by The Associated Board of the Royal Schools of Music
Adapted from *Time Pieces for Flute*, Volume 1, selected and arranged by Ian Denley (ABRSM)

The woman is fickle

La donna è mobile

from *Rigoletto*

Arranged by Nancy Litten

Giuseppe Verdi
(1813–1901)

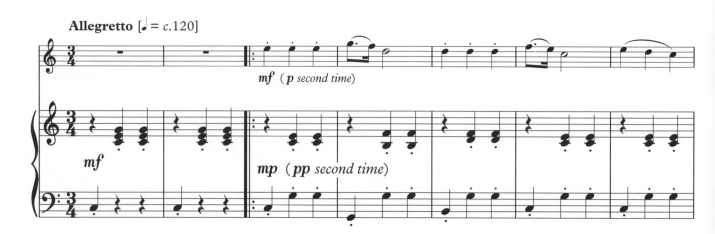

Verdi's 1851 opera *Rigoletto* is set in the 16th century in the north Italian city of Mantua. The plot centres on the arrogant, immoral Duke of Mantua, his court jester Rigoletto and Rigoletto's daughter Gilda. The aria 'La donna è mobile' is sung in Act III by the Duke in a tavern. The staccato markings in the melodic line help give the piece its swagger.

Lazy Sunday

from *Playaround* for Flute, Book 3

Roma Cafolla
(born 1949)

B:1

Fine

D.C. al Fine

Roma Cafolla is a Northern Irish composer. Amongst the large amount of educational music she has written are the graded *Playaround* volumes. The swung quavers give this piece a mood of weekend relaxation, but also notice the metronome marking: the piece may not be as lazy as you think!

© Forton Music 2014
Reproduced by permission from *Playaround* for Flute, Book 3.

B:2

The Easy Winners

Arranged by David Blackwell

Scott Joplin
(1867/8–1917)

Scott Joplin grew up in Texas, the son of a former slave, and became, as he called himself, 'the King of Ragtime Writers' – a pioneer in print of the ragtime style, which combines the regular tread of marches and dances with the syncopations of African American tradition. This is the first strain of a 'ragtime two-step', which he published in St Louis in 1901. The tempo marking 'Not fast' is an instruction which Joplin repeated in many publications. Note, too, that the classic ragtime style is not thought to have involved swung rhythms: even quavers give the piece its characteristic strutting movement.

B:3

The Pelican from Heligan

No. 1 from *Creature Comforts*, Grades 1–3

Mark Tanner
(born 1963)

D.C. al Fine

Mark Tanner is a well-known British pianist in concert halls and on cruise liners; he has also taught at school and college level, written reviews and articles for many magazines, as well as a book called *The Mindful Pianist*, and composed more than sixty albums of educational music. This is the first item in a graded collection of 'animal-inspired pieces': The Lost Gardens of Heligan are a popular visitor attraction in Cornwall, England, but the pelican is a rare bird in the county, so the title must have been chosen for its pleasing sound! The composer says that the piece is 'both quirky and fun to play; its recurring jaunty rhythms encourage quite a laid-back approach, but are best suited to a firmly rooted tempo.'

Study in F

from *Erster Flöten-Unterricht*, Op. 387

Wilhelm Popp
(1828–1903)

 C:2

Wilhelm Popp was a flautist of the court orchestra in his native Coburg, in central Germany, and later principal flautist of the Hamburg Philharmonic Orchestra. He published a vast amount of music for his own instrument – as you can see by the opus number of his *Erster Flöten-Unterricht* (*Flute Method for Beginners*), from which this study is taken. The character of the piece is established by its staccato markings and detailed phrasing.

Source: *Erster Flöten-Unterricht*, Op. 387 (Leipzig: Peters 1887). The dynamics are editorial suggestions only. The staccato dots on the final crotchets of bars 7 and 13 are editorial.

C:3

Snow Walk

No. 1 from *42 More Modern Studies for Solo Flute*

James Rae
(born 1957)

The British musician James Rae is a performer on clarinet and saxophone, a teacher, and the composer of over 120 volumes of music for student wind players. This is the opening piece in a second volume of studies in a variety of musical styles 'designed to improve the student's musical as well as technical abilities'. The piece is in G Dorian mode. The moderate tempo helps to suggest the feeling of trudging through snow.

Scales and arpeggios

SCALES

from memory
tongued *and* slurred

Scales and arpeggios

ARPEGGIOS

from memory
tongued *and* slurred

one octave ♪ = 72

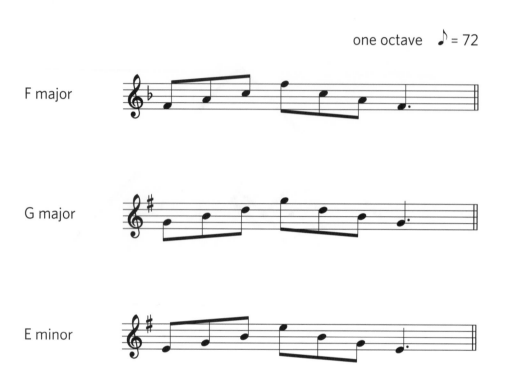

F major

G major

E minor

Sight-reading

Sight-reading

Sight-reading